KU-026-073

Who killed
Kit Marlowe

GALWAY COUNTY LIBRARIES
WITHDRAWN FROM CIRCULATION

To Aileen Bintliff

First published in 1996 by Franklin Watts

This paperback edition published in 1997

Franklin Watts
96 Leonard Street
London
EC2A 4RH

Franklin Watts Australia
14 Mars Road
Lane Cove
NSW 2006

© Terry Deary 1996

The right of Terry Deary to be identified
as Author of the Work has been asserted
by him in accordance with the Copyright,
Designs and Patents Act, 1988.

Series editor: Paula Borton
Designer: Sally Boothroyd

A CIP catalogue record for this book
is available from the British Library.

ISBN 0 7496 2621 6 (pbk)
0 7496 2181 8 (hbk)

Dewey Classification 942.05

Printed in Great Britain

Who killed Kit Marlowe

A History Mystery

by

TERRY DEARY

Illustrations by Linda Birch

W

FRANKLIN WATTS
LONDON • NEW YORK • SYDNEY

GALWAY COUNTY LIBRARIES

Contents

J 72,507 / 942·05

£3·50

Introduction

History is full of mysteries. Stories are passed down through the years and most of us believe them simply because they are written in books. But sometimes the writers get it wrong! History writers have been known to . . .

- make mistakes
- exaggerate
- invent 'facts'
- leave out important facts
- tell whopping great lies

This makes your job of understanding the past very tricky.

What is the truth? Who is telling it?

When a detective sets out to discover the truth he may have to solve a mystery. He must ask questions and work out who is lying and who is telling the truth. In this book that's just what you have to do. Become a history detective.

You will be given some fascinating facts mixed with some fascinating lies. Sort them out and solve the mystery. This *History Mystery* is arranged in three parts . . .

Part One

To make the mystery more enjoyable to read, it has been re-told in the form of a story. Imagine yourself in the shoes of two young detectives. Travel back in time and see how they uncover the evidence.

Part Two

To help you understand the world in which the mystery is set, there is then a selection of facts about the people of those days and their lives. Some of these facts will help you solve the mystery, others are simply fascinating facts on their own.

Part Three

Finally the story ends with the characters reaching their own 'solution' to the problem. You might not agree with their solution – some historians would certainly disagree! But remember . . . it is *a* solution, not *the* solution. In history there is hardly ever such a thing as *the one* right answer. That's why history is so strange and irritating and enjoyable and infuriating. History is a mystery . . . and *that's* a fact!

Part One

The story of Kit Marlowe

1

I drifted out of a deep sleep with two words chasing each other through my head.

Cold fire.

That was senseless. *Cold fire.* I tried to laugh. It hurt.

I tried to open my eyes. They seemed glued shut and I wanted to rub them with my hand. I couldn't find my hand.

At last I forced my eyes open. Above me was blackness. To my left the dull red glow of a fire. I turned my head. It hurt. The glow came from a fire in an iron basket on my left. In the basket there were iron pokers. Their tips glowed red but their handles were cold. *Cold fire.*

My left side was scorched by the fire. My right side was frozen by the damp air of my prison. *Cold fire.*

It smelled of the damp and the smoke . . . *bright smoke* . . . another pair of witless words. How could smoke be bright? And where had I heard those words?

I could taste blood in my mouth where I had bitten into my lip. I tried to roll on to my left side so my frozen right side could feel the warmth of the fire. I couldn't move.

My arms were stretched above my head and my feet were fastened to the bench I was lying on. I gave a small whimper of pain as my shoulders burned with the sharp pain. Then I began to remember. I wasn't lying on a bench.

I was lying on a rack, a crude instrument of torture. Ropes fastened my hands and feet. The ropes were wound around a wheel. When that man turned the wheel my body would be stretched. I felt that one more turn would break me.

He had promised to come back later. He had stirred the fire with the irons and left them to heat up. "One last chance," he said. One last chance to tell him the truth or he would begin to use those irons. *Cold fire.*

The thought made me shiver and the shivering made my stretched joints ache. The trouble was I couldn't tell him anything. I'd already told him everything I knew. He simply wouldn't believe me. He'd be back soon.

I was just fourteen years old. I knew I would not live to see fifteen.

I heard a soft creaking of the key turning in the lock of the door. A faint yellow light spilled over me from the torches in the corridor outside. There was the sweet smell of fresher air. Then someone whispered my name.

"John?"

Cold fire. I remembered where I'd heard those words before! That's when I passed out again.

* * *

I was standing in a large courtyard. It was a square, cobbled space where almost five hundred people could stand. The Swan Inn, two storeys high, surrounded the courtyard. In front of me a wooden platform had been built up. On the platform some men and boys were practising a play.

The spring sunshine was weak but the building sheltered me from the chill breeze from the River Thames. Still, I shivered a little. I always felt nervous before I went on stage. I straightened my wig and smoothed my dress for the twentieth time. It was the first time I'd worn my costume – this was the last rehearsal before the public came to see us. A *dress* rehearsal . . . and *my* dress was a poor fit. When I fell on to the tomb in my death scene it would split,

I felt quite sure of that.

"Feathers of lead, bright smoke, cold fire, sick health!" Richard sighed on stage.

"No, no, no!" the writer cried. He was standing on the cobbles surrounded by the rest of the company who weren't on stage. His hands were full of loose sheets of paper and he was scratching at the lines with a goose-feather pen. He stepped forward to the edge of the stage. "Richard," he said. "You are a young man . . ."

"I know," Richard answered stupidly.

"You are a young man called Romeo. A tough, fighting man even though you are only sixteen years old. Romeo likes going out with his friends and making trouble in the streets. Suddenly, he finds himself in love. In love with Juliet. His world is turned upside down. Nothing makes sense any longer. Where he was strong before, now he is weak. His heart was light as a feather – now it's heavy as lead; his future was clear and bright – now it's clouded like smoke; before he was cold and unfeeling – now he is hot and excited. *Feathers of lead, bright smoke, cold fire, sick health.* Do you understand, Richard?"

"Yes, Mr Shakespeare."

"You are in love and you are *angry* that love has done this to you. So, say that line as if you are an angry, confused young man."

"Yes, Mr Shakespeare."

"Don't say it as if you are a limp cabbage leaf," the playwright cried.

The rest of the company laughed. Richard turned red with anger. He spoke the line again, "Feathers of lead, bright smoke, cold fire, sick health!" and this time he said it furiously. Will Shakespeare smiled quietly into his papers. He had made Richard angry and the anger made him perform the way the playwright wanted. Mr Shakespeare was clever like that.

I wandered towards the inn door so I could come on to the stage from inside the building as I would in the next day's performance.

The girl was standing in the doorway watching the play. I'd seen her there every day when we rehearsed. She had a thin sharp face and dark suspicious eyes. From her apron I guessed she worked at the inn, but no one seemed to mind that she spent so much time watching our rehearsals.

As I tried to walk past her she muttered, "You look stupid." I stopped, unsure that I'd heard her correctly.

"Pardon? Were you speaking to me, miss?"

"I'm not miss. I'm Eleanor. You can call me Ellie."

I didn't know why I'd want to call her anything! I tried to walk past her again.

"I said, you look stupid," she repeated. This time she said it clearly.

"What do you mean?"

"A boy, dressed up in a wig and a skirt. Stupid!"

"I'm an actor," I said coldly. "I am playing the part of Juliet in this play." I couldn't help adding proudly, "The *leading* role."

"I still say it would be better if a real girl played the part," she sniffed.

I sighed. "Women and girls are not allowed to perform on stage. Women's parts are played by boys."

"Not very well," she said.

"What do you mean?" I asked.

"I *mean* you don't *move* like a girl," she said. "Maybe you've got a girl's voice, but I've never seen a girl *move* like you do. Not unless she had her feet screwed on backwards."

I tried to ignore her as I walked into the cool darkness of the inn and round to the back of the stage ready to make my entrance. What an irritating girl! But her words made me practise the way I walked. She was right. That was what was so annoying. My walk *was* all wrong. Suddenly I heard my cue to enter for the next scene, "Juliet!"

I had to step through the curtain that covered the door, skip on to the stage to meet my nurse, played by Will Kemp, and say, "How now, who calls?"

I rushed at the curtain, pushed it aside and cried, "How now . . ." That was when I stepped on the hem of my dress, tripped and hit the wooden stage hard with my hands and knees. My wig flew off and landed at Mr Shakespeare's feet. He picked it up and held it out as if it were a dead rat. As the other actors tried to smother their giggles, the playwright sighed heavily and stroked his bald head.

"You think *I* need a wig more than you?" he asked.

"No, sir," I mumbled, stuck the hideous curls back on my head and stumbled through the rest of the scene.

That Eleanor girl was watching me from the shadow of the doorway and her dark, cruel eyes forced me to make mistakes in every line and at every move.

At the end of the four-hour rehearsal Mr Shakespeare said to me kindly, "Perhaps we'd better talk about your performance this evening at supper."

"Yes, sir," I nodded and hurried off to change.

When Richard's voice broke, he couldn't play women's roles any longer. He'd moved on to play young men like Romeo. This was my one chance to prove I could act before my own voice became too deep. It began to look as if I'd lose that chance. I felt sure I wouldn't play Juliet the next day.

I didn't know how true that was.

2

"Sit down, John," Will Shakespeare said.

I sat across the table and waited for him to tell me I was no good for the part. Instead he said, "Food? You must be hungry."

"Thanks," I said.

He looked to the doorway. The Ellie girl walked forward. He smiled at her. "Could we have some more of this excellent mutton stew?" he asked.

She brightened and her sharp face was almost soft as she said, "Of course, sir."

"Now, John," he began. "This play is very important to me. Queen Elizabeth herself may wish to see it . . ." He noticed my startled look and laughed, "But not at tomorrow's first performance! It will have to be *perfect* before we let her majesty see it."

"Yes, sir."

"So, don't worry too much, John. You will be fine tomorrow. There is a superstition in the theatre that a bad dress rehearsal means a good first performance."

The Ellie girl returned with a plate of food for me and I pulled my knife from my belt to eat it.

"Thanks," I said to her, but she didn't seem in a hurry to go.

Will Shakespeare waved his spoon under my nose and

began talking eagerly. "One day I hope to be the best playwright in England."

"But you *are*!" I said.

He shook his head impatiently. "No, there was one who was a much finer poet than me. But I am learning, John. Maybe *Romeo and Juliet* is not as good as *his* best plays, but I am getting close to him."

"Who was he, sir?" I asked, and used a spoon to scoop up some of the gravy.

"Kit Marlowe. Christopher Marlowe to give him his correct name. Have you ever seen any of his plays?"

"I saw *Tamburlaine* about five years ago," I said. "And I acted in *Doctor Faustus* before I joined your company."

"Then you'll know how great he was!" Will Shakespeare cried. He shook his head again. "What a loss! What a loss! If he was still alive there's no telling how great he could have become. He would make my poor plays look like a schoolboy's."

"Did he die of the plague, sir?" I asked. The last outbreak had been two years ago when I was living at home in Canterbury.

"No," the playwright said and he stroked his neat beard. "He . . . was killed in a scuffle. An accident with a knife."

Suddenly, from the shadows of the small room, the girl whispered, "So they *said*."

Will Shakespeare didn't seem too bothered by her presence. "Aye, so they said."

"You mean you don't believe it was an accident?" I asked.

"I mean it was very suspicious. No one has ever got to the bottom of it, though it happened two years ago," he replied.

"It's a bit of a mystery, isn't it?" Ellie asked and stepped forward into the evening light from the window.

"Aye," the playwright admitted. He pulled a roll of papers from the pile on his writing table. "Sometimes I think his story would make a play. Look at my notes and tell me what you think."

I unrolled the parchment carefully. The writer's scrawling notes were mixed with some printed papers and letters written by someone else. "Where do I begin?" I asked.

"Act One, Scene One," the playwright chuckled. "My notes on his background. Read them and see what you think." He stood, picked up his hat and walked out of the room.

I tilted the papers so they would catch the evening light and began to read. Ellie looked over my shoulder, just to annoy me, I'd swear.

3

The first paper was a copy of a report from the inquest.

"They always have an inquest if there's a suspicious death," Ellie said.

"I know," I said shortly.

"What does it say?" she asked.

I read the report aloud. *"It happened that Christopher Marlowe met with a certain Ingram Frizer and Nicholas Skeres and Robert Poley, at a house in Deptford. They met at the tenth hour before noon, on the thirtieth day of May, in the thirty-fifth year of the reign of Queen Elizabeth* – Elizabeth came to the throne in 1558, so the thirty-fifth year of her reign was 1593 – *in a room in the house of a certain Eleanor Bull, widow. They passed the time together there and dined. After dinner they walked together quietly in the garden belonging to the house. At the sixth hour after noon they returned from the garden to the room and ate supper together there."*

"And my mother says I talk too much," the girl exclaimed. "Imagine talking for eight *hours*! I wonder what they had to talk about?"

"I don't think the report mentions what their meeting was about," I said, scanning the document quickly.

"What happened to Kit Marlowe, then?" Ellie asked. I read on.

"After supper Ingram Frizer and Christopher Marlowe argued

and exchanged angry words since they could not agree about the payment of the sum of pence – the reckoning."

"Mrs Bull must have charged them for the food and the rent of the room," Ellie said. "I know most of the inn-keepers in the Deptford area but I haven't heard of her. She must just have a lodging house – rent rooms and sell meals. Why couldn't they come to a public house like ours? They'd have paid for their food but not for a room."

"Maybe they wanted to talk in private," I said.

Ellie shrugged. "So they argued about the money for the rent of the room and the food. Probably a bit drunk, if I know actors and playwrights," she muttered.

I ignored the remark and read on. *"Christopher Marlowe was lying on the bed in the room where they had supped. He moved angrily against Ingram Frizer as they exchanged these angry words. Ingram Frizer was sitting in the room with his back towards the bed where Christopher Marlowe was lying. He was sitting at a table with Nicholas Skeres and Robert Poley sitting on either side so that he could in no way escape."*

"That's strange, isn't it?" the girl put in. "You don't usually turn your back on someone you're arguing with, do you?"

I continued, *"Christopher Marlowe suddenly drew Ingram Frizer's dagger which was at his back and with the same dagger Christopher Marlowe gave Ingram Frizer two wounds on the head to the length of two inches and the depth of a quarter of an inch. Ingram Frizer, in fear of being slain and sitting between the other two in such a way that he could not escape, struggled with Christopher Marlowe in self-defence. He tried to get the dagger back from him and it so happened that, in the struggle, he gave Christopher Marlowe a wound over his right eye to the depth of two inches and a width of one inch. From this wound the said Christopher Marlowe then and there instantly died."*

Ellie stood up and walked to the door. She began to pace out the action. "You be Frizer and I'll be Kit Marlowe," she said. "I walk behind you, snatch the knife from the back of your belt and you are trapped at the table."

She raised an imaginary knife and brought it down into my back. "Frizer was cut on the head," I reminded her.

"I know," she said. "That's what's so strange. I could stab you anywhere I want. Why do I cut you on the head? It doesn't make *sense*. No wonder Mr Shakespeare is interested in the story."

"What happened to Frizer, I wonder?" I said, turning to the next sheet in the wallet.

"Probably hanged him for murder," Ellie said.

"No," I said. "Look at this. It's a copy of a pardon."

"You mean Frizer killed the playwright and got away with it?" she said.

"Read it for yourself," I said.

She picked it up and read it quickly. I wondered how a serving girl learned to read so well.

"It's a repeat of the story told at the inquest," she said. "Then it goes on, '*We are therefore moved by pity to pardon Ingram Frizer for the death.*' It's a queen's pardon dated the 28th of June. He spent four weeks in jail then went free."

"Free to murder again?"

"So you think it was murder?" the girl said quietly. "Why?"

"I don't know," I replied, irritated. I was irritated by my own thoughts as much as by Ellie. "It's just a feeling I have," was all I could say.

"There are just two possibilities," she said thoughtfully. "Either Marlowe was mad or drunk and attacked Frizer the way he said . . . or Frizer deliberately

GALWAY COUNTY LIBRARIES

murdered him as he lay on the bed. A knife in the eye is reckoned to be the best way of assassinating someone."

"How do you know?" I asked, startled.

"Oh, I've lived all my life at the Swan Inn."

"You have?"

"Yes. You don't think I'm just some sort of serving maid, do you?" she asked and tilted her chin up.

"Er . . ."

"My parents own the Swan. I help out when we're busy – like when we have a visit from travelling players."

"I see," I nodded. So *that* was why she could read so well and had time to watch us rehearse.

"When it gets dark we see some of the lowest life in London. The *underworld* we call it. Every criminal you can think of passes through here at some time."

"Aren't you afraid?" I asked.

She laughed. "So long as they behave themselves when they're in here they can do what they like. But I learn a lot from listening to them. I could probably cut your purse without you knowing," she said and smiled a clever smile.

"Or cut my throat?" I asked.

"If I had to," she shrugged.

I thought about it for a while. "You know so many villains, you think you can tell when there's something criminal going on?" I waved the paper at her. "Like the death of Kit Marlowe?"

"No. I have to admit, I cheated a little. I suspect Frizer and Skeres because I know them. They're too crafty to be caught by a drunken attack."

"This man Poley said that Marlowe started it," I reminded her.

"I don't know him," Ellie admitted, "but if he's a friend of theirs he would lie to save Frizer's grubby skin. If they're in the taproom tonight then I'll let you see for yourself," she promised.

4

I'd never met a murderer before. But Frizer didn't look like
a man who lurked in alleyways and stained his hands with
innocent blood. His doublet and breeches were of dark blue
velvet, slashed to show a paler blue satin lining. His cloak
was richly embroidered and his sword had glittering stones
set into the handle. His face was too long to be handsome
and his eyes rather close but he didn't look a villain.

His little friend Skeres, on the other hand, had watery
eyes that slithered round the room as he talked and a
mouth so thin you could barely make out his lips. His skin
was moon-pale and moon-cratered with smallpox scars.

When Ellie spotted them she made a plan for me to get
into conversation with them. I'd dressed in some poor and
ragged clothes that she said a dead customer had left. From
the smell of them he'd died of the plague. My skin crawled
at the feel of the rough wool against my skin. "They've
been washed," the landlord's daughter insisted. I didn't
believe her.

She said if I paid her a groat then she'd add a drug
to their wine that would loosen their tongues. I paid her
the four pennies then watched her serve the two men
as they sat in a gloomy alcove at an ale-washed table. After
half an hour Frizer was unlacing his doublet a little as
he relaxed. Even Skeres's slithering eyes were sliding

around no faster than a snail's.

Ellie had taught me my lines and rehearsed me more thoroughly than Mr Shakespeare ever did. Finally I was ready to play my part.

"Good evening, sirs," Ellie smiled at the killer and his partner.

"Evening, my pretty," Skeres leered. "Who's your little friend?" he said, fixing an ugly eye on me.

Ellie leaned forward and whispered conspiratorially, "A boy who would like to work for you. He works for the travelling actors and he knows some of the fools who waste their afternoons watching the plays. The sort of fools who will fall for your little money-lending trick."

Frizer spread his hands wide, "Tricks, my dear! Mr

Skeres and I are honest businessmen."

"Right," Ellie said briskly. "If you don't want John to help you then you can find some poor mark for yourselves!"

"Wait!" Frizer cried. He smiled at me and showed his yellowing teeth. His breath smelled of the same tobacco that stained those teeth. Richard once loaned me his pipe to try this smoking. He said doctors recommend it. I was sick.

"Sit down, my boy. I'll explain."

I sat opposite him and Ellie slowly filled their wine goblets again so she could stay and listen. Frizer gulped his greedily, wiped his mouth on his sleeve and said, "We are money-lenders, you understand. The law says we should lend money but not make a profit. Now that's not fair, is it?"

"No," I agreed.

"So, we have a little arrangement. Let's say you need a hundred pounds. We agree to lend it to you. You sign a paper saying you will pay us back that hundred pounds . . . or we will take your house instead. Is that fair?"

"That's fair."

"When you have signed the paper we say we don't have the hundred pounds. We say we will give you something worth a hundred pounds instead. What did we give that mark last year, Skeres?"

"Some old cannon from Tower Hill," his partner chuckled.

"They cost us next to nothing. The mark can sell the stuff . . . but usually he asks us to sell it for him. We tell him we got just fifty pounds for the cannon. He takes the fifty pounds because he is desperate for money. Then we make sure he pays us back the hundred pounds he agreed to pay. We lend fifty and get a hundred back. Fifty profit for us!"

"Doesn't he object?" I ask.

"Object! Of course he objects! Some of them even try to take us to court. But we always win, you see. We know the law. We don't break the law, do we, Skeres?"

"No, Frizer. We never break the law," his little friend chuckled.

This was the moment Ellie had been waiting for. "Don't they ever get violent when they find they've been tricked?" she said as she wiped the table carelessly.

"They threaten," Skeres giggled.

"Is that what Kit Marlowe did?" she asked.

I thought Frizer was going to choke on his wine. The smile vanished from his face. The first expression was one of anger, then he tried to hide it under a mask of uncaring boredom. But I'm an actor – an expert on expressions. He didn't fool me. Ellie's comment had struck some nerve under that hard shell of his.

"Kit Marlowe was a ruffian," Frizer growled.

"I thought he was just a poet and a playwright," Ellie said carelessly.

"So you didn't know about his brawling and fighting?" Skeres added.

"No," I said.

Skeres looked pleased with himself as he listed Marlowe's crimes. "Do you not know about the Hog Lane murder? A poor young man called Bradley was walking down Hog Lane on a September afternoon when he met Marlowe. They hated one another and it is *said* that Bradley began to attack Marlowe – but Bradley isn't around to give his side of the story. I think it's as likely that Marlowe started the fight. Anyway, as they fought, along came Tom Watson – Marlowe's best friend. Watson tried to separate them and he was wounded. Bradley turned on Watson and drove him back to the roadside ditch. Watson drove his sword into Bradley's chest and he died instantly."

"*The blood is spilled of my dear friend,*" I said.

"What's that?" Frizer asked.

"It's a line from a play Will Shakespeare wrote. There is a street fight with three men. One tries to come between the other two and one is killed. I wonder if Mr Shakespeare knew about the Marlowe fight when he wrote the story of Romeo?" I said.

"He's bound to. Everyone knew it. But Marlowe got away with just a few weeks in Newgate Prison," Frizer said a little bitterly. "Have you ever been in Newgate?" he asked me suddenly.

"No."

"If you are lucky then you come out with nothing worse than a few rat bites. But you can't sleep for the cold and the moaning of the prisoners with jailfever. You can't eat the hard bread they give you and you can't breathe the stinking air. You can barely see in the light of a single candle set on a black stone. That's what Marlowe suffered before he was released. Would that teach *you* a lesson, boy?" Frizer asked.

"Yes, sir," I told him.

"Then you're a cleverer man than Marlowe. Just a few months later he was arrested in Canterbury for fighting a duel with a man called Corkine. All over some silly insults. No one was hurt that time, but that's your Kit Marlowe for you. Hot-tempered and violent."

He sounded like some of the characters in *Romeo and Juliet* who fought and died on the streets. "*For now, these hot days, is the mad blood stirring,*" Will Shakespeare had said. It sounded as if he had lost his temper with Frizer and fought, just as he had with Corkine and Bradley. This time he had come off worse.

Marlowe had a violent life and died a violent death. No mystery, I decided. I was about to leave.

Maybe I should have done. It would have saved me a lot of pain.

5

That's when the loose-tongued Skeres said, "Of course he was up to all sorts of trickery, wasn't he, Frizer?"

Frizer seemed suddenly sober. He looked at Skeres as if he could have cut his throat. Then he looked at me, "He means young Marlowe had problems with the law in other ways."

"Forgery," Skeres put in, unable to stop himself from talking.

"Aye. Forgery," Frizer agreed.

"But the punishment for forgery is hanging," I said. "He can't have been guilty."

Frizer looked uncomfortable. "He probably learned to make fake coins when he was in Newgate. He was locked in a cell with a forger called Poole. Marlowe tried to make some fake coins when he was over in Holland, but a friend betrayed him and he was sent back to England for trial."

"They found him not guilty, then?"

"Marlowe had friends. Powerful friends. He got away with that crime too," Frizer said.

"Who were these friends?" I put in. Maybe Marlowe's death had something to do with his other crimes.

"Best not to ask," Frizer said. He sat back on the bench and swigged more wine. He closed his eyes and slowly his head rolled to one side. His mouth fell open and his wine-stained tongue hung out.

"A bit too much in that last glass," Ellie said softly with a pained smile.

But little Skeres was still eager to talk. "And of course he was in trouble at the time Frizer stabbed him. But you'll know all about that?" he said, and his watery eyes rolled.

"For forgery? For fighting?" Ellie asked, sitting down next to me to listen.

"No," Skeres chuckled. "For bl . . . bla . . . blasphemy!" He managed to get the words out at last.

"For speaking out against the Church?" Ellie prompted him.

"That's right. Mind you, he was a bit unlucky," the little man said and his frog mouth gave a hard smile. "It all started with the Dutch church scandal. Three weeks before Marlowe died, someone pinned some poetry on the wall of the Dutch churchyard in Broad Street. It said that the Dutch and all the foreign merchants should go home. Stop taking the hard-earned money of the English. Get out or there'll be trouble, it said."

"What sort of trouble?" I asked.

"Riots in the streets, attacks on the Dutch merchants or their houses, that sort of thing."

"And Marlowe wrote that? That isn't blasphemy," I said.

Skeres looked annoyed. "Listen, boy, will you? Just listen! Somebody *found* the verses and took them to the constable of the watch. The verses were written in the same rhythm that young Marlowe and young Shakespeare use to write their plays. Then there was a line about how the massacre of the Dutch would be worse than the massacre in Paris . . . and of course Kit Marlowe wrote a play called *The Massacre in Paris*."

"I know," I said.

"Then the paper was signed 'Tamburlaine' . . . and we

all know who wrote the play *Tamburlaine*, don't we?"

"Kit Marlowe."

"Exactly!"

"But if Kit Marlowe wrote those verses he wouldn't be stupid enough to give so many clues as to who he was," I objected.

Skeres sighed. "Did I say Marlowe wrote the verses? Did I?"

"No, but . . ."

"And did I say he was arrested for it?"

"No-o."

"So are you listening to what I'm saying?"

"Yes, Mr Skeres."

"What I said was that it *started* with the Dutch church scandal and that Marlowe was just a bit unlucky. Isn't that what I said?"

"Yes, Mr Skeres."

"So, the government went into a bit of a panic about these verses and the threats. They ordered the officers of the law to arrest any suspects. They gave permission for the officers to search any rooms or chests for papers. They even gave them permission to torture any suspects until they talked. Ever seen the torture instruments in the Bridewell prison, boy?"

"No, sir."

"You'd better hope you never do. They start by standing you on a stool and chaining your arms above your head. Then they take the stool away and leave you hanging there." He gave a sharp cackle. "After a night of that you're usually ready to talk. Then there's the Duke of Exeter's daughter . . ."

"What does she do to you?" I asked.

Ellie exploded with a short laugh. "It's not a 'she'. It's another name for the rack they stretch you on!" she hissed.

"Oh, sorry," I said.

"Then there's thumbscrews and there's hot irons. Most people talk when they're on the rack, though," Skeres said nodding, to himself.

"And they tortured Marlowe?"

"No . . . I'm coming to that. They searched the room of some other play-writer. Someone called Thomas Kyd. Heard of him?"

"He wrote *The Spanish Tragedy*," I said.

"They were searching Kyd's rooms and they found some papers. Some religious writing. And these writings said terrible things. They said things like, Jesus wasn't the son of God . . . blasphemy!" Skeres' eyes rolled with the horror of it. "Kyd said the papers didn't belong to him. He didn't even know they were there! He said they got mixed

up with his papers a year or two before, when he was sharing a room with another young play-writer. They must belong to him! And who was that other play-writer?"

"Kit Marlowe," Ellie said.

"Kit Marlowe," Skeres nodded. "He was in Kent at the time of the search. They arrested him and brought him back to London. He had to report to the queen's council every day. When the council were ready they would begin questioning him. And we all know what that means. . ." the man leered.

"Torture?"

"Probably. That's what happened to Kyd . . . tortured. In fact he never recovered from the treatment. He died just a year later," the little man babbled. "In fact, old Frizer here did Kit Marlowe a favour. He killed Marlowe before the government got their torturing hands on him."

"And before he talked," Ellie murmured. "If Kyd dropped Marlowe in trouble then who could Marlowe betray under torture?" she whispered to me.

"I don't know," I said.

The girl looked at me pityingly. "His powerful friends, clay-brain! Remember he had powerful friends in high places!"

I thought about it. "So these powerful friends paid Skeres and Frizer to assassinate Marlowe before he talked!" I gasped.

"Sounds more likely than that story about an argument over the bill," Ellie said.

I looked at Skeres. His head was nodding forward and about to drop into his wine. "Mr Skeres . . . where will we find Richard Poley?"

He looked up through half-closed eyes. "Poley? You don't want to talk to Poley."

"Why not?"

"Dangerous man – a spy!"

6

Ellie and I left Skeres and Frizer to sleep off their drugged drinks and walked across the courtyard to the dressing room behind the stage. The rich costumes glittered in the candlelight and the blunted swords hung from their belts. Not real swords. Make-believe like everything in the world of the theatre.

On a table stood the props – the things we needed on stage. Ellie picked up a small blue glass bottle and toyed with it as she walked up and down. She talked as much to herself as to me.

"Kit Marlowe died after an argument over money."

"We only have Skeres' and Frizer's word for that. They're such a pair of rogues they would make up any sort of story," I told her.

"Right. So, they murdered Marlowe for some reason. Why?"

"Because he was one of their marks. They'd tricked him out of money and he was becoming a nuisance?" I suggested.

"No," she said. "They said they know the law. They always won – they didn't need to murder him."

"So," I persisted, "Marlowe was a forger. They fell out over some crooked deal."

"Possible," she admitted. "Or Marlowe was a

blasphemer and he was murdered to keep his powerful friends out of trouble . . ." Ellie stopped walking and studied the bottle in her hand. "What's this?"

"The bottle of drugs that Juliet drinks in the play."

Ellie's eyes sparkled with excitement. "Why didn't we think of that?" she cried. "Listen! If Kit Marlowe's friends are really powerful they could have saved his life!"

"Sorry, I don't see how."

"You're an actor!" she cried. "I've watched you play Juliet. How does she escape the dreadful torture of marrying a man she hates?"

I shrugged. "She fakes her own death with the drugs that are supposed to be in that bottle."

"That's it! Marlowe was in the theatre world. Maybe he just *pretended*. Maybe Frizer and Skeres helped him to fake his own death so he could get away safely. It's like something out of one of Mr Shakespeare's plays! The powerful people promised Frizer he wouldn't be charged . . ."

" . . . and he wasn't!" I said, understanding her excitement now. "Marlowe would be alive and well and still writing those marvellous plays. Maybe that's what Will Shakespeare thinks. That's what he hoped we'd discover."

"All we have to do is find Marlowe," she said and her face was glowing. "It must be safe for him to come back now."

"Where do we start?" I asked.

"Kent. That's where he was living with his friends before he was arrested. We'll go tomorrow!" she said.

"Ellie! I'm acting in *Romeo and Juliet* tomorrow. It's my best role yet. I'm not missing it for a hundred Marlowes."

She pulled a face of disappointment. "Pity. You look pretty stupid dressed as a girl anyway."

"So you said," I replied stiffly.

"I'll go myself then," she said and marched out with a swirl of skirts.

I picked up the candle and followed her to the door.

"We've forgotten one thing!" I tried to tell her. She didn't turn or even pause. "We haven't had a chance to talk to Poley yet! The dangerous man – the spy." The girl disappeared into the door on the far side of the courtyard and I was left alone with the candle and the damp night air.

I sensed a movement behind my back. Before I could turn something was thrown over my head and the candle fell from my hand. The material was rough like sacking. The arms were like bands of metal round my chest.

I gasped and sucked in a mouthful of the dusty foul air from the sacking. I tried to cry, "Help!" but first a large hand clamped over my mouth then something solid hit me on the back of my head. The dark of the hood was replaced by the deeper darkness of unconsciousness.

I drifted awake from time to time and realised I was fully inside the sack now. It had been swung over the man's shoulder and he was hurrying through the night streets. I groaned. "You'll be quiet," he said in a low voice, "or you'll earn yourself another slap across the skull with my cudgel," he promised. I stayed quiet.

The man was a little unsteady and he wasn't too careful with me. I was battered against the walls of the houses we passed and I groaned with the pain.

"Quiet!" he said again. This time I knew the voice. It was Frizer, the man who might be Marlowe's murderer. The sleep in Ellie's tavern must have been an act too. I'd been stupid to imagine I was the only actor sitting at that table.

My head throbbed and I felt sick. It was quiet on the streets and I knew that a man like Frizer could easily avoid the night watch. We stopped suddenly and I heard the watch cry out just a few streets away. "Twelve of the clock, look well to your locks, your fire and your light, God give you good night." Then we moved on with only the steady splash of the man's feet in the mud and the dirt of the streets.

At last I felt we were climbing some stairs. Frizer swapped words with someone. There was a clatter of keys and a creaking of opening doors. I was dropped to the floor and the sacking was torn off me.

I'd been thrown into a bare, stone-walled, windowless room. I shivered in the darkness and listened to the scutter of rats breaking the silence.

It must have been morning before they came and dragged me out. I was briefly blinded by the sunlight in the corridor before being taken into another room lit only by a glowing basket of fire. Before I could look at my new surroundings my hands had been bound and I was dragged across to a bench. As the man tied me hand and foot to the wheels he chuckled and said with mock politeness, "Allow me to introduce you to the Duke of Exeter's daughter!"

I twisted my neck to see what he was doing. He seemed to be fitting a wooden lever into the wheel of the rack and pulling it. The ropes went tight and I felt a sharp pain in my arms as my muscles were stretched. I gave a sharp cry and the man laughed. "Oh, we haven't even started yet, Master John. Not even started. By the time we take you off here you'll be a foot taller!" he sniggered. "Unless you decide to talk."

"Talk about what?" I groaned. "I've done nothing!"

"You'll admit to everything after a dance with the Duke of Exeter's daughter," the man said viciously.

Then another voice came from the shadows. "That will do. Leave him to me now."

I had thought Frizer was a simple villain and I was wrong. But there was no mistaking the owner of the new voice. He was as cold as my burning muscles felt hot and far more deadly.

Cold fire.

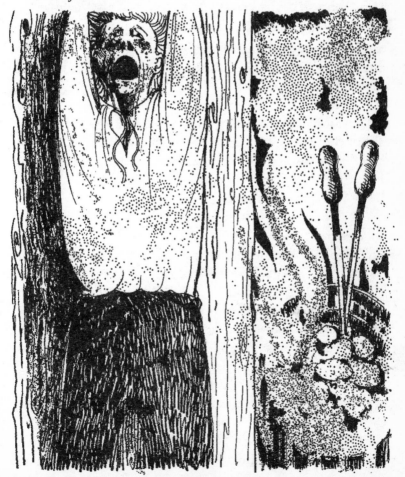

7

"Let us understand one another," he said quietly. "If you answer all my questions at once, then you will go free. If you do not, then my friend will keep turning the rack until you do. Is that clear?"

"Yes."

"Good. Now, why have you been asking questions about the death of Christopher Marlowe?"

"I was interested. I'm an actor. I've been in his plays. His story would make a good play," I said.

"Who are you working for?" he asked.

"The Lord Chamberlain's players," I said, naming the theatre company.

"No, no, no," he said smoothly. "I mean, who sent you to spy on Skeres and Frizer?"

I was silent for a moment. I could hear the steady crackle of the fuel in the iron basket and the rustle of the man's clothes as he stood up.

"Really, this is not good enough," he said, and picked up the wooden lever. My mouth went dry.

"No one sent me!" I croaked.

I heard the lever slotted into the wheel and felt ropes begin to pull again. "No one!" I shouted.

"Let us try an easier question, shall we?" he said. He was leaning over me now but I could not make out his face in the shadows of the fire-glow. A hat shaded his eyes and I could see some dark hair escaping from underneath it. "What have you discovered about Marlowe?"

"He was a violent man . . . had a temper . . . easily got into fights. He was a forger but he was never punished . . . he has powerful friends . . . I don't know their names."

"Are you sure?" he asked. "No!" I cried quickly, before he had the chance to turn that wheel any further.

"Anything else?"

"He was accused of blasphemy . . . after some notes were found in Thomas Kyd's room," I said. "He died before he could be brought to trial for that."

"And how did he die?" the man asked.

"He fought with Frizer . . . in the struggle Frizer stabbed him in the eye."

"And do you believe that?"

I thought about it. I wanted to lie but knew it would be useless. "No," I said. "I don't believe it."

"So, Frizer killed Marlowe deliberately?"

"Yes . . . or . . ."

"Or what?"

"Or he pretended to kill him. They put some other body in Marlowe's place and made up the story of the fight."

The man gave a soft laugh. "Oh, no, Master John. Kit Marlowe was stabbed all right. I know. I was there."

"Poley? You are Poley?"

"Yes, young man, and you seem to know altogether too much. I will leave you here a little while to think about your story. Maybe I'll return later and use some of these branding irons to tickle your memory. If you tell me the truth, then I'll set you free. If you don't, then I'll kill you. Do you understand?"

"I'm telling the truth!" I cried.

"We'll see," he said and disappeared into the shadows.

I heard the door unlock and then the keys rattle as it was locked behind him.

I was left there for hours. I had a sudden and ridiculous new fear. I was going to miss the afternoon performance of *Romeo and Juliet*. I'd let the whole company down. Mr Shakespeare would make sure I never worked in the theatre again! On my cold right cheek I felt the warm gush of tears. Somehow that performance meant more than the threat to my life. I tried to take my mind off the pains by running through my lines. That was when I fell asleep – or swooned with the pain, I'm not sure which.

When I awoke, those lines from the play were still going through my head. *Cold fire*.

* * *

I heard a soft creaking of the key turning in the lock of the door. A faint yellow light spilled over me from the torches in the corridor outside. There was the sweet smell of fresher air. Then someone whispered my name.

"John?"

I passed out and was wakened by water being splashed on my face. "John!" the voice said urgently.

A girl's voice. That girl. "Ellie?" I tried to say, but my voice was barely a croak.

I heard her fumbling with the ropes. She cursed as she struggled and in the end pulled out a small knife and cut them. "Quickly, get up!" she said.

I rolled onto my side and tried to pull my legs underneath me. They wouldn't obey me. I fell on to the floor and my arms weren't strong enough to stop me. Ellie was talking to me in a fast but gentle voice all the time. Encouraging me and urging me on. She placed her hands under my arms and lifted me up so I was sitting on the bench. Then she pulled a bundle from a bag at her feet.

"Put this on," she ordered.

"Whatsit?" I croaked.

"A dress." She saw I couldn't manage it so she pulled it over my head and fitted my arms into the sleeves. Then she pulled a long wig on to my head and dragged me to my feet. My legs wouldn't support my weight so she threw one of my arms around her shoulder and practically carried me to the door.

The guards were dozing happily. "My special wine," she murmured, then dragged me down the torchlit corridor. "Keep your head down," she said. "You're upset. Your brother has just died in prison."

"I haven't got a brother," I burbled.

"Pretend. Act! You're an actor, remember? Not a very good one, but an actor," she had to add.

When we reached the guard at the gate she stopped, "Juliet is so distressed she's practically fainting away."

"Here, let me help you," the guard said, and swept me off my feet and cradled me like a baby. He carried me out to the street where a cart was waiting.

That saved me the effort, but I felt the wig begin to slip. He laid me gently in the cart and I felt Ellie's hand pull the wig back in place before she turned to gush her thanks to the kind man. I think she promised him a year's supply of her special wine if he ever cared to visit the Swan!

The driver turned to look at me. "John?" he whispered. "We'll get you home in no time. Hang on, lad."

I squinted up at him. The evening sun hurt my eyes. "Thank you, Mr Shakespeare," I managed to say before I passed out again.

GALWAY COUNTY LIBRARIES

8

When I awoke it was late. Ellie was sitting at one side of the bed in the Swan waiting to spoon soup down my throat. Mr Shakespeare was sitting at the other side frowning at me.

"The play?" I croaked.

"Oh, it went ahead and was a great success," the playwright said impatiently. "But you, John. How are you? I'm so sorry to have drawn you into this terrible danger. I should have realised that men who would kill Marlowe would be savage enough to harm anyone asking questions. We're like flies to ruthless boys," he said. "They'll kill us for their sport."

"Marlowe had powerful friends," I said weakly.

"And so does Poley, it seems. I think that's what Kit's death was all about. He was caught in the war between two powerful groups."

"But what was the war about?" Ellie demanded.

Will Shakespeare reached for his leather wallet and slipped out a sheet of parchment. "I think the answer lies in this paper," he said. "Kit Marlowe went to Cambridge University. Just before he was due to receive his degree someone objected. Said he'd missed too many lectures."

"Too busy writing plays?" Ellie asked.

"I'd have thought so. But it seems the accusation was that he'd gone to the Rheims Catholic College in France and was therefore a traitor – remember the Catholics have laid lots of plots against Queen Elizabeth."

"So, he was a traitor?" I asked. "That's why he died?"

"No, that's where this letter is important. It is a letter from the queen's council itself, explaining why Kit Marlowe was *not* a traitor. Read it."

My arms were too weak to push myself up on the mattress. Ellie helped me to rise and read the document in the pale light of the candle.

"To the masters of Corpus Christi College, Cambridge. It has been reported that Christopher Marlowe had gone to Rheims

College in France and had planned to remain there. We hereby certify that he had no such intent. In all of his actions he has behaved in a regular and wise manner. He has performed Her Majesty good service and deserved to be rewarded for his faithful dealing. The Queen's Council request that any rumours should be crushed and that he should be given the degree as soon as possible. Her Majesty requests that anyone employed on her business should not suffer from the opinions of people who are ignorant of her affairs."

"Strong stuff," Will Shakespeare said. "The Queen is giving a very sharp lecture to the masters of Cambridge."

"And when you remember what Skeres said about Poley, it all fits," Ellie said.

"What does?" I asked. My own aching brain could make little of it then. "Will you be able to write Kit Marlowe's true story now, Mr Shakespeare?" I asked.

He stroked his fine, pointed beard. "I don't think so, John. I think we should let Kit Marlowe rest in peace. His wonderful plays are what he will be remembered for."

"So his death will remain a mystery to people in the future?" Ellie asked.

Will Shakespeare nodded.

"It's a mystery to me." I was bewildered.

The playwright laughed. "You have all the clues you need to solve it now. You're just too weary. We'll explain tomorrow morning," he promised. He rose to his feet. "Sleep well, Romeo," he grinned. "Your Juliet here will watch over you."

"What devil art thou, that dost torment me thus," I muttered, quoting one of Juliet's lines.

"Sleep dwell upon thine eyes, peace in thy breast," Ellie answered, quoting Romeo.

I slept.

Part Two

The Fact Files

1. THE PEOPLE FILE

Who can you believe? Here are some true facts about the main characters in the story. What sort of people are they? Can you trust what they did or said?

Christopher (Kit) Marlowe

Name: *Christopher Marlow* – on an early print of one of his plays *Christofer Marlin,* or *Marlen, Marly, Marlyn, Marlye* and *Merlyng* – at his Cambridge college *Christopher Morley* – at the inquest into his death *Christofer Marley* – on his arrest warrant *Christofor Marloy* – in the only copy we have of his signature, dated 1585

Appearance: Long brown hair brushed back, pale round face, beard along the line of the jaw and fine moustache.

Character: Intelligent. He was born in 1564. His father was a shoemaker with a large family. He went to King's School, Canterbury, and then Cambridge because he was clever, not because he was rich. His plays are great works for such a young man. If he had lived as long as Shakespeare he might have been a greater writer. He was always short of money and his plays did not earn him much, so he became a spy when still at college. He was hot-tempered and fearless.

Problem: Marlowe escaped several tricky situations. Would he have let himself be trapped by enemies and murdered? Would he have attacked a man over the price of a meal? Or would he have faked his own death to escape his troubles?

Ingram Frizer and Nicholas Skeres

Name: *Ffrancis Frezer*
– in the record of
Marlowe's burial
Nicholas Skyrres

Appearance:
Unknown

Character: Two men
who made money any
way they could. They
were spies for the
English government.
They also bought and
sold property at a profit and they were dishonest money-lenders to innocent victims. They always won their cases in court but there's no doubt they twisted the law to suit themselves.

Skeres was almost certainly part of a cruel and clever plot to have Mary Queen of Scots executed and her friends tortured to death – the Babington Plot. Skeres was named (two years after Marlowe's death) as one of "a number of masterless men and cutpurses, whose practice it is to rob gentlemen's chambers and shops, in and about London". He was a member of the criminal world, often called the "underworld".

Problem: Would these two men have been part of a deliberate plot to murder Marlowe? They were dishonest, but were they murderers? Or were they simply unlucky to be in the same room as Marlowe when he flew into a drunken rage and attacked Frizer? And if they were, then why didn't Skeres do anything to help Frizer? Would Frizer have been heartless enough to kill an unarmed man?

Robert Poley

Name: *Robert Pooley*
Robyn Poley

Appearance: Unknown

Character: A very experienced spy for the English government. Worked as a secret agent for at least twenty years before the death of Kit Marlowe. He was a suspected (but not proven) poisoner. One of his greatest successes was tricking Anthony Babington into betraying himself. As Babington's last letter to him said, "Farewell, *Sweet* Robyn (if you have been true to me) or the most *evil* creature on Earth (if you have *not* been true to me)." Poley had *not* been true, so "most evil creature" was the right description. Poley was so crooked that his own masters didn't trust him! He even boasted about being a liar, saying, "I will swear to anything so long as it gets me out of trouble."

Problem: Would this man have made arrangements to have Kit Marlowe killed – knowing Marlowe was a fellow spy in the service of Elizabeth I? And, if he did, would he have taken the risk of being present at the murder? Would he have had the power to promise Frizer a queen's pardon if he knifed Marlowe? Would he have gone to Marlowe's inquest and told lies about the stabbing?

William Shakespeare

Name: *William Shakespere* – on the title-page of one of his plays. Since then there have been over eighty spellings of his name from Shagspeare to Shakestaffe. There are six examples of his signature, all spelled differently, but he never spells it *Shakespeare.*

Appearance: Dark hair beginning to go bald on top, long at the back. Neat beard, large dark eyes.

Character: A great playwright, like Kit Marlowe, and just a few months younger. Marlowe began writing first and Shakespeare must have been influenced by plays like Marlowe's *Tamburlaine.* Like Marlowe, he moved to London (about 1587) to make a living from the theatre but he was a calmer character than Kit. He was also a better businessman and made a good living from the theatre, acting in as well as writing the plays. Shakespeare was married with children and came from a fairly well-off family in Stratford. It's been said that he left Stratford as an outlaw after being caught poaching a deer . . . but that may not be true.

Problem: Would William Shakespeare have been part of a plot to allow Kit Marlowe to disappear? Marlowe had to appear dead – and a dead man can't write plays! Would Shakespeare have agreed to put his name to plays written by Marlowe? Could he have spent twenty years as England's best-known playwright and kept that secret?

2. THE TIME FILE

Nothing in history is ever simple. Marlowe's death was one event in a time trail that began before he was even born . . .

1533 King Henry VIII wanted a son to carry on the family name of Tudor. But his wife, Catherine of Aragon, had a daughter – Mary Tudor. Henry decided to divorce Catherine and try another wife. The Catholic Church did not agree  with divorce, so Henry replaced the Catholic Church with the Church of England, which followed the new Protestant teaching. He married Anne Boleyn and she had a child, Elizabeth. So . . .

1536 Henry had Anne Boleyn beheaded and married Jane Seymour. . .

1537 she had a son, Edward. Then she died.

1539 Henry had closed all the monasteries and made himself a lot of money by selling their land and treasures but . . .

1547 Henry died. Edward took over and tried to make the new church even stronger until . . .

1553 Edward died. His eldest sister, Mary Tudor, took over. She was a Catholic like her mother and wanted to make the Catholic Church strong again. She had Protestants burned and . . .

1554 married the Catholic King of Spain, Philip. A Spanish Catholic King of England? Not popular. But . . .

1558 Mary died. Her Protestant sister, Elizabeth, took over. It was up with the Protestants and down with the Catholics again. Of course, Elizabeth was always worried that

Philip of Spain would claim the throne – after all, he was supposed to be King of England. He would need many Catholic friends in England to make this work. Who were these Catholics? What were they up to? Elizabeth needed spies to keep an eye on the Catholics. Meanwhile . . .

1564 February, Christopher Marlowe was born. He would grow up to become a great playwright and spy. In April the same year William Shakespeare was born. He would grow up to be a great playwright too.

1568 Mary Queen of Scots had problems in Scotland and fled to England. She asked Elizabeth to give her shelter. Elizabeth offered her a prison! After all, Mary Queen of Scots had a claim to the English throne . . . *and* she was one of those feared Catholics. Spies were needed to keep an eye on her too. Finally . . .

1587 some Catholic plots to set Mary Queen of Scots free and overthrow Elizabeth were discovered, so Elizabeth had Mary executed. A year later . . .

1588 the Catholic plan for Philip to invade England finally took place. The great Armada brought thousands of soldiers from Spain. Luckily for England, Elizabeth's navy defeated them . . . this time! But, would they be back? Spies were needed more than ever, including a young playwright called Christopher Marlowe. He worked as a playwright and a spy until . . .

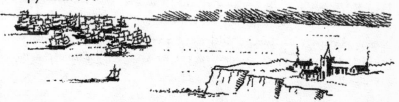

1592 . . . a dreadful plague killed thousands of people in London. The theatres were closed to prevent it spreading. Playwrights were out of work. Some, like Shakespeare, made money from writing poetry instead. Some, like Marlowe, made money by doing more spying until . . .

1593   Christopher Marlowe was killed in a meeting with three other spies. They said it was an accident. But was it? This meant . . .

1594   that when the theatres opened again, William Shakespeare was the most experienced and successful playwright in England. He was sponsored by Elizabeth's court until . . .

1603   Elizabeth died. The end of the Tudors, but not the end of Tudor terror and torture. The English throne was taken by James I, the son of Mary Queen of Scots. He was a Protestant, so the Catholics were not too happy and in . . .

1605   they plotted to blow James up as he opened Parliament. The gunpowder plot failed and the plotters, including Guy Fawkes, were tortured and executed. Another victory for the government's spies against Catholic plotters.

1616   William Shakespeare died in retirement in his Stratford home and might have been forgotten by everyone but . . .

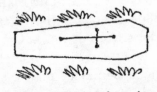

1623   Shakespeare's friends published his plays in the form of a book. The publisher said the great plays were not for the Tudor age but "for all time". We'll never know how great Marlowe's plays could have been because he died so young. The victim of a trail of terror that had started with Henry VIII.

3. THE LIFESTYLE FILE

The character of boy-actor John is fictional, but there were many actors who would lead that sort of life. Would you have enjoyed it?

The terrors of the Tudor theatre

Visiting the theatre seems to be a quiet and respectable pastime. But in Tudor times it could be anything but!

If you were an actor. . . The poorest spectators stood around the stage to watch. Because they stood on the ground they were called 'groundlings'. They paid a penny to watch. If they were bored they would simply chat to the people around them and ignore you. If they were *really* annoyed with your performance they might throw their fruit or nuts at you.

If you were a spectator. . . Richer members of the audience would pay two pence to sit in the galleries – rows of seats around three sides of the stage. The richest would pay six pence to sit in 'boxes' – private seats right next to the stage. Some special guests could even sit on the edge of the stage itself. At one performance a spectator on the stage blocked the view of someone in a box. They began to fight while the actors were trying to perform their play. It ended when the man on the stage drew a sword and stabbed the man in the box . . . the audience thought this was more fun than the play!

Even if you could not afford to sit on the stage, being a spectator could still be dangerous. At a performance of Marlowe's *Tamburlaine* in November 1587 there was a very tragic accident. In the play the actor playing the governor of Babylon is tied to a post and shot. The actor firing the gun aimed to miss, of course. At that particular performance he did indeed miss . . . but killed a woman in the audience!

If you were a theatre owner. . . During a performance of Shakespeare's *Henry VIII* a real cannon was used to fire blank shots. Unfortunately the blanks contained cloth which  caught fire and drifted on to the thatched roof of the theatre. The building burned to the ground. When it was rebuilt the theatre company (sensibly) had the roof covered in tiles.

If you belonged to a theatre company. . . Plays were not very popular with the people who ruled the city. A Protestant preacher once said, "Sin causes the plague and plays cause sin. So plays cause the plague." City councillors complained that the plays brought crowds together and caused all sorts of problems like . . .

✗ fighting and street disturbances
✗ robberies
✗ keeping people from going to church
✗ accidents with collapsing stages
✗ spreading the plague

Theatre companies had to have a respectable sponsor, or the actors could be arrested for being tramps and beggars. When the theatres were closed (after accidents or an outbreak of plague) the actors struggled to make a living. They could go on tour if the London theatres were closed. But touring cost money so their wages were cut to half. Even the Earl of Pembroke's famous company struggled during the plague year of 1593. They were forced to sell their costumes and their play books so they could eat. It's easy to see how out-of-work actors could turn into 'rogues, vagabonds and sturdy beggars' and why the law treated them with suspicion.

Theatre companies on tour would do anything for money. They would even give private performances. A man called Gamaliel Ratsey offered a travelling company forty shillings to perform for him. The actors were thrilled – their most successful shows usually earned them just twenty shillings. They performed, as promised, and Ratsey paid them. The next morning they set off happily for the next town on their tour but were stopped in a nearby forest. A highwayman held them at gunpoint. "You are nothing but a band of thieves," he told the actors. "Now, pay me the forty shillings you stole from Ratsey!" The miserable actors handed the money over. How did the highwayman know about their performance the night before? Because it was Ratsey himself who was the highwayman. (The actors probably had the last laugh. This story was published when Ratsey was hanged for his thieving ways.)

If you were a playwright. . . Playwrights mixed with some fairly rough people. Many of their acting spaces would be used for plays one day and bear-baiting or prize fighting the next. Shakespeare made clever use of this. In *The Winter's Tale*, he brought one of the tame bears on stage to chase a character off. But the violent friends that theatre people had could cause problems. Playwright Ben Jonson was a spy, like Marlowe, and had a part in the arrest of Guy Fawkes in 1605. Jonson killed a man in a sword fight but was set free by the courts.

Playwrights made very little money from their plays. They

were paid just once for the script. The theatre companies could then perform it as many times as they liked and make a lot of money from it but the writer never got another penny. As a result playwrights had to find other jobs – as Shakespeare and Marlowe did – or write an awful lot of plays to make a living. Shakespeare made his money from acting or owning theatres, so he made do with writing a couple of plays each year. Thomas Heywood worked for the Queen's Players from 1605 to 1619 and claimed to have written 220 plays. That's a play every three weeks! Many Tudor playwrights died at an early age – if a knife didn't kill them then exhaustion did.

   Writing plays could be a dangerous business! Marlowe, Shakespeare and Jonson all spent time in prison for writing plays which annoyed people in authority.

Plays can carry ideas and if the ideas upset the queen or king then the playwright would be blamed. The Earl of Essex and his friends plotted to overthrow Elizabeth I. They hired Shakespeare's company to perform *Richard II* – a play all about a monarch being overthrown! Elizabeth was furious and Shakespeare was lucky not to lose his head!

How to be a Tudor spy

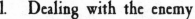

If life in the theatre seems rough, would you rather have made a living as a spy? Try this simple test to see if you would make a Tudor spy.

1. Dealing with the enemy

John Story was a Catholic and worked hard for Queen Mary. When Mary died and Elizabeth came to the throne, Story escaped to Holland where he made a nuisance of himself. He began searching English ships and taking away any Protestant books the English wanted to smuggle into the country. How would you stop him?

a) Send more books and hope that some get through.

b) Complain to the Dutch about his behaviour, and ask them to arrest him so he can be sent to prison.

c) Send an English ship to Holland full of Protestant books. Let him know they are there. He will step on board to take them. Kidnap him and take him back to England.

2. Carrying secret messages

James Painter had to carry messages from Paris to London and back for the English government. There was always a chance that the mail would be stolen and read by an enemy. How did James Painter keep his messages secret?

a) He carried them inside his jacket, not in the mail bag.

b) The messages were written in code.

c) Painter memorized the messages so he did not have to write them down.

3. Keeping messages secret

Codes can be broken, of course. If you were worried that the enemy might have a copy of your code then you had to find another way to write a message. The answer was to use invisible ink. The paper looks harmless enough in normal light, but if it is heated (or dipped in a chemical) then the secret message shows through. What do you use for invisible ink?

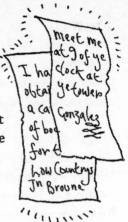

a) Water

b) Milk

c) Urine

4. Catching enemy messengers

A Spanish dentist is travelling through England. You suspect that he is carrying secret messages from Spanish Catholics to English Catholics. What do you do?

a) Ask him politely if he is spying and suggest that he goes home.

b) Search his dental equipment and arrest him if you find secret letters.

c) Search his dental equipment and let him go if you find secret letters.

5. Winning friends

Your master, the Earl of Essex, has had a row with Elizabeth I. How can you help him win back her favour?

a) Work extra hard to uncover plots against the queen.

b) Tell the queen there is a plot to kill her and that you have prevented it.

c) Tell the queen there is a plot to kill her – then torture people until they back up your story. Accuse her doctor of trying to poison her and torture him until he admits it . . . even though he had no such plan. Have him executed.

Answers

Mostly a) answers – hopeless! Become a roadsweeper, an innkeeper or a coalminer . . . anything but a spy!

Mostly b) answers – you will be a useful employee for the government, but leave the spying to somebody else.

Mostly c) answers – you are nasty, twisted, untrustworthy, cruel and hardly human. You will make an excellent Tudor spy!

Notes

1.c) The spy, William Parker, was *also* arrested and locked in the Tower of London with John Story. That way Story *thought* he was locked up with a friend and chatted quite freely to Parker about all the other Catholic plots he was involved in.

2.c) It is believed that Painter had a special method of memorizing complicated messages.

3.c) Milk *could* be used but rarely worked as well as urine. Onion juice and orange juice were also used.

4.c) Once you have found his hiding place then it's best to let him go on carrying messages because you can find which English traitors he is working with. In fact the dentist hid letters in a secret compartment in a mirror. A spy called Bisley had messages sewn into his buttons!

5.c) The Earl of Essex wrote, "I have discovered a most dangerous and desperate treason to bring about her majesty's death. The executioner was to be Doctor Lopez and the manner poison." The earl got his information from a spy called Andrade. It was a lie. Elizabeth didn't really believe her doctor was trying to kill her, but he died a horrible death anyway.

A plot to kill a queen

You can't just kill a queen and expect to get away with it. You have to have a very well-organised plan. In 1586 there was a Catholic plot to kill Elizabeth I. The plot was in three parts:

1. Organise an invasion of Catholic armies from France, Spain, Italy and Scotland. Have English Catholics ready to support them as soon as they land.

2. Release Mary Queen of Scots from prison where she has been held for over fifteen years. She can be a new Catholic Queen of England. After all, she is Elizabeth's cousin and has a claim to the throne . . . when Elizabeth is dead. So . . .

3. Kill Elizabeth I. A man called John Savage has vowed to kill her and six 'gentlemen' have agreed to help.

One of the plotters was a young man called Anthony Babington. The plot was named after him even though he wasn't the most important plotter . . .

The same Robert Poley who was there when Marlowe was killed. Poley was Marlowe's friend . . . but Poley was Anthony Babington's friend. And look what happened to Babington!

This was the world of the spy. If a useful spy, like Christopher Marlowe, became a nuisance, then what would the spy masters do? Tell him to behave himself? Or have him murdered? What do you think?

Or was Marlowe a victim of the stealing, cheating and cruel criminals of the Elizabethan underworld?

Criminal capers

London in Kit Marlowe's day was a dangerous and violent place to live. The criminal world even had its own language. Can you match each word to its modern meaning?

Word
1. bite
2. boozing ken
3. cony
4. copesmate
5. cozen
6. cuttle bung
7. fullams
8. gentry-cove
9. peck
10. yarrum

Meaning
A. milk
B. gentleman
C. knife for cutting off a purse
D. trick dice
E. alehouse
F. food
G. trick
H. money
I. partner
J. the victim of a trick

Need some clues? Here's a trickster's diary . . .

"I followed the *cony* in the *boozing ken* because I hadn't had the chance to use my *cuttle bung*. My *copesmate* bought the *gentry-cove* some *yarrum* and *peck*. Then they played dice. Of course we used *fullams* to *cozen* him out of his last *bite*."

Still puzzled? Then here are the answers . . .

bite = money; **boozing ken** = alehouse; **cony** = the victim of a trick ('cony' was another name for a rabbit); **copesmate** = partner; **cozen** = trick; **cuttle bung** = knife for cutting off purses; **fullams** = trick dice; **gentry-cove** = gentleman; **peck** = food and **yarrum** = milk.

Five ways to grab a groat

People in Tudor England lived hard lives, mostly working on the land. But there was a new group of people coming together in the cities. They lived on the profits of crime. They lived in their own world.

It was a world that Kit Marlowe knew quite well: an underworld.

If a time machine dropped you in Elizabethan London could you survive as a criminal? Here are five ways they used to make money . . .

1. Bung-nipping

Elizabethan gentlemen hang their purses from their belts on string. Using your *cuttle bung* (knife) you can cut the string and grab the purse full of money. Of course, gentlemen know you are around and they keep a hand on their purse most of the time. What you need is a *copesmate* (partner) to help you distract the victim. Your partner can have a *counterfeit crank* (pretend to have a fit). While the *cony* (victim) is trying to help your *copesmate*, you can *nip* (cut) his *bung* (purse). A good place to *nip* a *bung* is St Paul's Church in London where crowds gather every day for business meetings or simply to meet friends. It is at the heart of the city and after cutting a purse you can easily get lost in the crowds.

2. Wandering minstrels

Another popular place for bung-nipping is the theatre. If the play is a really exciting one by Shakespeare or Marlowe then the audience are watching the stage . . . that's when you 'take care of' their purses! The Elizabethan law says you have to stay in the place where you were born – unless you are a nobleman. The only way to travel round the country is to have a 'passport' from your local lord, giving you permission. Actors like Shakespeare would become servants of a rich lord, and be allowed to travel. Having this freedom to move around means you are in a good position to do some thieving. Entertainers are often invited into homes and have a great chance to steal something while they are there. Or they may play at a local inn, gather large crowds . . . and share the money the cutpurses have made from robbing those crowds. Travelling entertainers are often closely involved with criminals and treated with great suspicion. Would Kit Marlowe have had a lot of cut-purse (and cut-throat) friends?

3. Conjuring

Collect money by inventing some clever trick that will draw crowds of people. If they enjoy it enough they will pay money to watch. A juggler called Kingsfield showed the body of 'John the Baptist' who'd had his head cut off – the head lay at the feet and it spoke! A similar trick is to take a bladder and fill it with sheep's blood. Disguise the bladder to look like your stomach and chest and fasten it under your shirt. Then announce you will stab yourself in the stomach. When you stab, the bag bursts, the sheep's blood flows out and the audience are astounded that you are still alive. Of course you need a strong shield under the fake stomach so you don't stab yourself. (A drunken conjurer once forgot the shield – he stabbed, staggered out into the churchyard . . . and died!) Would Kit Marlowe's friends in the theatre be able to rig up a *fake* stabbing like this? Mrs Bull and other witnesses would say that Marlowe was dead – he could then escape the threat of torture and prison. Or, like the case of the drunken conjuror, did this little trick go horribly wrong?

Did you know . . . ? William Shakespeare used the idea of herb cures in his play *Romeo and Juliet*. Juliet takes a herb which makes her sleep so deeply that she appears to be dead. If Shakespeare knew of such a herb then Marlowe must have done. Would he have tried a similar fake death? In *Romeo and Juliet* Shakespeare describes the herb mixer's shop in which:

a tortoise hung,
An alligator stuffed, and other skins
Of ill-shaped fishes; and about his shelves
Green earthen pots, bladders and musty seeds.

Hardly the sort of place to pass a public health inspection these days!

4. Cheating law

Elizabethans enjoyed gambling – even though Elizabeth tried to pass laws to prevent it. A game of dice seems simple enough. All you do is bet on the numbers that will come up when the dice are rolled. But clever gamblers use trick dice – there are at least fourteen types of dishonest dice. One, called a *bristle*, has an almost invisible hair sticking out of one face. Of course the dice could never land on that face because of the hair. The real art is to get the *cony* into your game in the first place. Here's a simple trick: drop a coin on the ground where he can see it; as he goes to pick it up then claim you saw it at the same time; suggest you split the money, half each; call into the nearest alehouse to buy a drink; say this will get some change so you can share the money; once he's in the alehouse then ask him if he fancies a game of dice with your newly found money. Now you have him! Cheat at dice – not only take the 'found' money back from him – take all his own money too!

5. Cozening at cards

If you aren't so good at dice then try cheating at cards with a pack that is 'marked'. The marks can be tiny pin-pricks or nicks in the edges of the cards. Now you know the cards the *cony* is holding, you can't lose. To get your *cony* to bet a lot of money then bring in a friend as a *barnacle*. Your *barnacle* will lose lots of money at first and the *cony* will see himself winning a pile of coins. Still the *barnacle* doubles his bets every time. When the pot of money is really large then the *barnacle* suddenly wins it (and shares it with you later, of course). A man who loses a lot of money and finds he has been cheated will become very angry – even violent. One report on Marlowe's meeting at Mrs Bull's house says the men were playing backgammon. Would Skeres and Frizer be the sort of men who would try to cheat Marlowe? And, if they did, was Kit Marlowe the sort of man to lose his temper and start a fight to the death.

Mumchance at cards

Here is a simple Elizabethan card game. Card cozeners often played it. You can play it against friends – for points, not for money.

You need:
- ✗ a pack of playing cards
- ✗ two or more players

To play:
- ✗ each player calls the name of a card – everyone must name a different card
- ✗ the cards are turned over one at a time
- ✗ the player whose card is turned over first wins a point
- ✗ first to ten points is the winner.

Painful punishments

What if you were caught in some of these crimes? What sort of punishments would be waiting for you?

The laws were harsh and you could be arrested for many crimes – including begging or just the suspicion of being involved in witchcraft. If you were found guilty then the punishments could be particularly harsh.

Prison
Richard Vennor's story. . .
"This prison's a fine and comfortable place – if you can afford it. When the sergeants dragged me in here I paid to have my own cell. I paid for food and wine. But, when my money ran out, they threw me in 'the Hole'. Unless I can get free I'll die in here. I sleep on bare boards with fifty other men. Wherever you look some poor soul lies groaning in sorrow, the child weeping over his dying father, the mother over her sick child. In winter the cold will kill you. In the warm summer weather diseases multiply in the filth and they'll kill you. If you survive the cold and sickness then hunger will get you. The play-writer Dekker said that in the Hole you are 'buried before you are dead'. That's me. My crime? I sold tickets for plays – plays that were never performed. I pocketed the money. Never let yourself be taken to prison." Richard Vennor died in prison.

Pressing
Margaret Clitherow's story. . .
"I thought I was clever. They asked me if I was guilty or not guilty. I refused to answer. So they lay me on the floor and place a board over me. Then they gradually

pile weights on top of me until I can stand no more and give them an answer. Of course, if I plead guilty then they'll take me out and execute me. If I plead not guilty then they'll force my family to give evidence against me . . . then they'll execute me. My crime? I am a Catholic and refuse to go to Queen Elizabeth's Protestant Church. A servant betrayed me. Never let yourself be pressed." Margaret Clitherow died in 1585.

Whipping and the stocks
Eliza Morton's story. . .

"I was desperate. Without food or money I ended up at the Bridewell in London. Some call it the poor house. They take you there if you have no money and no work. They give you the poorest food and a rough blue uniform. But when they questioned me they found I had a child. I had left the child in the streets of Southwark. I thought some kind soul might care for it better than I could. But my punishment for abandoning the child was to be whipped on my bare back. They used a whip of two cords with no knots in and gave me twelve strokes. After that I was dragged through the streets and locked in the stocks at Cheapside so the crowds could pelt me with rubbish and spit at me. A sign above the stocks announced my crime. Never end up in the stocks." Eliza Morton survived.

Manacles
Thomas Kyd's story. . .

"Richard Topcliffe is the queen's rack-master. We came to the torture room in a sort of procession, the guards walking ahead with lighted candles. The chamber was underground and dark; a vast shadowy place with every instrument of human torture

there. They pointed some out to me and said that I should taste them. I was put on a stool and my hands chained above my head. Then the stool was taken away. I hung there from eight in the morning till four in the afternoon. Then Topcliffe asked me if I would confess. My only crime was having a document that said Jesus was not the son of God. I told them the document must have belonged to Christopher Marlowe. What else could I do? Never end up in the manacles."
Thomas Kyd died within a year, probably as a result of his treatment by Topcliffe.

The Scavenger's Daughter
Thomas Coteham's story. . .
"I was arrested on 20 November 1581 and taken to the Tower of London. The torture instrument was brought to my cell. It was an iron hoop, hinged in the middle. I was tied with my knees up to my chin and my hands behind me. Then the hoop was clamped around me, crushing my knees into my chest. This machine is called the Scavenger's Daughter. I was asked to confess that I was a Catholic. I confessed. Then they asked me to confess that I planned to kill Queen Elizabeth. That was not true. I had only come to England to talk to other Catholics. We wanted Elizabeth off the throne – we did not wish for her death. Never end up in the Scavenger's Daughter." Thomas Coteham survived the torture . . . but was found guilty at his trial and executed.

Did you know. . .? In 1578 a foreign visitor summed up the English punishment system like this:

If a woman poison her husband, she is to be burned alive for petty treason; if a servant kill his master he is also to be executed for petty treason; he that poisons a man is to be boiled to death in water or lead, even if his victim does not die. In cases of murder all those who help the murderer are to suffer the pains of death by hanging. Many crimes are punished by the cutting off of one or both ears. Rogues are burned through the ears and sheep-stealers punished by the loss of their hands.

Kit Marlowe had been in prison for fighting in the street and for forging coins, but he had got away with both crimes. Was he now afraid of being punished for the document found in Thomas Kyd's room?

Kit Marlowe would know about the way Kyd was tortured. Prison might not frighten him . . . but some of the other things the queen's torturers could do would frighten the bravest person.

So, did the powerful Poley offer to help his loyal spying friend Marlowe? Was Kit so afraid of torture that he would try to fake his own death rather than go to the torture chamber? Would *you*?

Entertainment

Kit Marlowe lived in a cruel world. The theatre may seem like a gentle entertainment to us today. But in Marlowe's time the theatre buildings were used for some cruel sports when they weren't being used for plays. A visitor to the Beargarden theatre in 1584 described the scene:

There is a round building three storeys high in which are kept about a hundred large English dogs, with separate wooden kennels for each for them. These dogs were made to fight one at a time with three bears, the second bear being larger than the first and the third larger than the second. After this a horse was brought in and chased by the dogs and, at the end, a bull who defended himself bravely. Next a man threw some white bread among the crowd who scrambled for it. Right over the middle of the place a rose was fixed. This rose was set on fire by a rocket. Suddenly lots of apples and pears fell down upon the people standing below. While people were scrambling for the fruit some rockets were made to fall down on them from above. This caused great fright but amused the spectators. After this, rockets and other fireworks came flying out of all corners and that was the end of the entertainment.

Bear-baiting and bull-baiting took place just once or twice a week. The kind owners decided the animals needed a rest! On the animals' rest days plays were performed.

Not everyone enjoyed the theatre or the crowds it attracted. Very strict Christians, called Puritans, tried to object to theatres whenever they had the chance. Three years after Marlowe's death, James Burbage, a friend of Will Shakespeare, converted some old monastery buildings into an indoor theatre. The district council of Blackfriars was run mainly by Puritans. They were furious and wrote this letter to government ministers . . .

James Burbage has bought certain rooms at Blackfriars and means to turn them into a common playhouse. It will grow to be a very great annoyance to the inhabitants of Blackfriars. It will gather together all sorts of vagrant and wicked persons. They will come, pretending to see the plays, but working at all manner of mischief. Also there will be crowds of people cluttering our streets which would be dangerous if God sends us a plague. Besides, this playhouse is so near to the church that the noise of drums and trumpets will greatly disturb the preachers and the congregation when they are trying to pray.

Who do you think won the case?

Answer: The Puritans. Burbage was not allowed to open the theatre in 1596, although a company of schoolboys (the Children of the Chapel Royal) were allowed to perform there. In 1606 Shakespeare's company was finally able to put on plays there – and the Blackfriars theatre made him more money than his other London theatres.

In 1593 Marlowe, Shakespeare and their friends in the theatre had some powerful and determined enemies. Within fifty years of Marlowe's death the Puritans had closed all theatres in England. But would they really murder Marlowe to stop his plays?

4. THE FOOD FILE

....

If you'd like a taste of Elizabethan life then why not sample some of their cooking? Try this recipe and discover how Will Shakespeare might have eaten at an inn like the Swan . . . or what Kit Marlowe might have had for his last meal at Mrs Bull's house.

Mutton stew

Guests at an inn like the Swan would often enjoy mutton stew. Mutton was popular because sheep were plentiful in England. They were kept for their wool but also provided cheap mutton when they died. Very tough *old* mutton usually! So, the best way to make old mutton tender would be to stew it for hours.

The other good thing about stew was that it could be kept bubbling over the fire for hours and served into a dish when a customer asked for some. In good inns it would be cooked with tasty ingredients like lemon and expensive ingredients like sugar.

Ingredients
450g mutton leg chops
1 lemon
425 ml stock (use a stock cube)
50g currants
1 teaspoon wine vinegar
1 tablespoon of sugar
1/4 teaspoon of pepper
Red food colouring (cochineal)

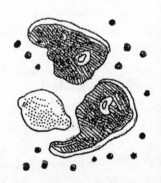

Method

Heat the stock in a saucepan until it boils.

Cut the meat into square pieces.

Slice the lemon then cut each slice into quarters.

Put the meat, the lemon, the currants and the pepper into the boiling stock.

Simmer for an hour and a half.

Just before serving add the sugar, the food colouring and the wine vinegar.

Serve in a bowl with crusty bread.

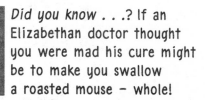

Did you know . . .? If an Elizabethan doctor thought you were mad his cure might be to make you swallow a roasted mouse – whole!

Terrible toothpaste

Sugar was a luxury in Tudor times, but if you could afford it then you'd eat it in large amounts. This is one of the reasons why people like Queen Elizabeth had such rotten, blackened teeth. The rotten teeth also made their breath smell bad, which is why they would have cleaned their teeth with a mixture like this.

Ingredients
2 tablespoons sugar
1 tablespoon honey
the peel from an orange
a small bone (such as a bone
from a lamb chop)

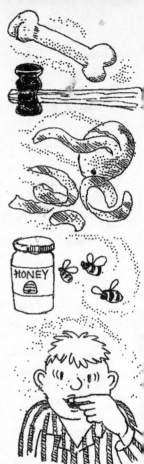

Method
Boil the bone until it's clean then
bake it until it's bone dry.
Put the bone in a paper bag and beat
it with a hammer until it's a powder.
Grate the orange peel finely.
Mix the bone powder, grated peel
and sugar. Stir in the honey to make
a thick paste.
Dip a finger into the paste and rub it
into your teeth and gums.
Then . . . either clean your teeth
properly with toothpaste and a brush
or repeat the Tudor toothpaste
treatment every day for two years . . .
and wait for your teeth to drop out!

Did you know . . . ?
Queen Elizabeth I was a terrible
coward about having her rotten
teeth pulled out. One of her
bishops had a tooth of his
own pulled out to show her
how painless it was! Rich
Elizabethans used toothpicks
made of precious metal.
So they would always be handy
they wore them in their hats.

5. THE EVENTS FILE

The death of Christopher Marlowe was just one small event in the Tudor age. His death was hardly noticed except by his friends. In the month of his death a plague killed 2,000 people. In those days a life was cheap and there were greater events occupying the minds of Elizabethan England . . .

The execution of Mary Queen of Scots

The first Tudor king was Henry VII. He won the throne by defeating Richard III at the Battle of Bosworth Field.

Elizabeth I was queen because she was Henry VII's grand-daughter . . . but Mary Queen of Scots was *also* the grand-daughter of Henry VII. No wonder Elizabeth was afraid of her!

Mary was ambitious and ruthless. Her first husband was murdered . . . then she married the man who probably murdered him! That was why she was thrown out of Scotland. Would she then plot to grab the throne of England from cousin Elizabeth?

Elizabeth decided she would, that's why she had her locked away for nearly twenty years. Even so, Mary tried to plot a Catholic revolution.

The English government's spies, like Poley and Skeres, uncovered the plot and saved Elizabeth. Mary couldn't be trusted. She had to die. But did she have to die so horribly?

Diary of an execution

Robert Wyngfeld was at the execution of Mary Queen of Scots. A few days later he wrote this report . . .

8 February 1587

Without any terror of the place she came into the hall and stepped up to the scaffold. A stool was brought to her. She sat down and began to pray very quickly in Latin. In the middle of her prayers she cried so much that she slipped off her stool. The two executioners kneeled down and asked her to forgive them. She answered, "I forgive you with all my heart." Then, with the help of her two maids she began to undress.

During this she smiled and said that she had never taken her clothes off in front of such a crowd of people. When she had undressed to her petticoat, the two women burst into pitiful shrieking and crying. The queen made the sign of the cross over them, said goodbye to them and prayed.

Then she laid herself upon the block most quietly and stretched out her arms and legs. At last, while one of the executioners held her straight with one of his hands, the other gave her two strokes of the axe before he cut off her head.

Some people say it took *three* blows to cut the head off. The executioner tried to pick the head up by the hair . . . but the bleeding thing fell to the floor. The hair he had grasped was a wig that came away in his hand. Mary's natural hair underneath was grey. From under the petticoats of the dead queen's body her faithful dog crept out, whimpering.

Did you know . . . ? In 1572 there was a plot called the Ridolphi plot aimed at putting Mary Queen of Scots on the English throne. That same year the Catholics in Paris murdered thousands of Protestant men, women and children. English Protestants must have feared the same would happen to them if Mary became the Queen of England.

The Ridolphi plot failed. Mary stayed in prison. But, almost twenty years after the Paris Massacre, an English playwright reminded the English people of the danger of the Catholics. He wrote a successful play called *The Massacre at Paris*.

You can imagine this play would make him a lot of enemies amongst the English Catholics. Who was the writer of *The Massacre at Paris*?

Christopher Marlowe. Would his Catholic enemies try to plot his death in Mrs Bull's house?

Queen Elizabeth had ordered the execution of Mary. Afterwards she apologised to Mary Queen of Scots' son for having his mother beheaded! In fact Elizabeth and many English people were pleased that Mary was dead – it was one less Catholic rival for the throne. But there was still another, Elizabeth's brother-in-law, King Philip II of Spain. A year after Mary was executed the English had to face a new threat from across the seas.

The fated fleet

The defeat of the Armada in 1588 is remembered as a great victory for the English navy. It was also a victory for the English spies who knew most of Philip's plans before his ships even left Spain. They didn't *know* when the Armada would sail or *where* it would land, but they knew the strength of its forces. Bonfires were prepared on hill tops to signal when the invasion started.

Although the English were ready for the Spanish – whenever they came – the Spanish helped in their own downfall. Their commander, the Duke of Medina Sidonia, summed it up in a letter to Philip.

When your Majesty ordered me to take command of the Armada, I gave your Majesty many reasons why I should not do so. This was not because I wanted to refuse. It was because I realised we were attacking a country so powerful, and with so many friends, that we'd need an even bigger force than the one you had gathered together. My health is bad and I am always seasick. The person in charge of the Armada should understand sailing and fighting at sea. I know nothing of either. Still, you ordered me to sail and I did. We are now half way to England at the port of Corunna and the Armada is already damaged. Many of our largest ships have gone missing. On the ships that remain there are many sick men. The number of sick will grow because of the bad food. Not only is it rotten, but there is so little that it will not last two months. I would ask your Majesty to decide if we should continue this voyage. Remember the huge army you gathered to attack Portugal – and many of the Portuguese were on our side. Well, sire, how can you expect us to attack England with the force that we have now? All of these problems and dangers can be avoided. Simply make peace with the English now.

The commander of the invading army, the Duke of Parma, agreed with Medina Sidonia and also wrote to Philip . . .

The foot soldiers are ready and together. But the cavalry are scattered around the country since there was not enough fodder here. I am doing my best to keep up the spirits of the troops. Still, the foot soldiers only number 18,000. Even with the 6,000 coming with the Armada we will still have a weak force. Sickness will mean we shall have even less. I wish your Majesty could have let me have more men. We are also short of pilots who know the crossing to England. Without them we could not attempt to invade England.

Philip refused these requests and doomed many Spanish soldiers and sailors to death. Less than half of the 130 ships returned to Spain.

The Armada

If there had been newspapers in Elizabeth's time they might have gloated over the defeat of the Armada . .

No Harm-ada!

June 1588

HER HAPPY HIGHNESS, Queen Elizabeth, today praised our brave boys in blue for their defeat of Philip's flops. For years the Spanish bullies have been preparing this attack on our little island. For years old Philip II of Spain has claimed he should be our Catholic king. And when his evil ally, Mary Queen of Scots, got the chop last year it was the last straw. He started building the biggest navy the world has ever seen – the mighty Armada.

It was big Phil of Spain against little Liz of England. But little Liz had the best ally of all. She had God on her side. That's right. God has shown himself to be an English Protestant not a Catholic. Just look at the way God smiled on the English and brought foul luck to Phil :

✗ Super Spanish admiral, Santa Cruz, died just a week before the Spanish were due to sail. The Spanish had to make do with the poor old Duke of Medina Sidonia – foul luck, Phil!

R.I.P.

✗ The Spanish fleet set sail for the Netherlands to join up with his army there. Many were wrecked in storms before they even got there. And our super spies knew all about the crazy king's plans so Drake and Howard's fleet were waiting for them – foul luck, Phil!

✗ The brave English fleet couldn't stop the Spaniards reaching the coast of the Netherlands. But when the Armada got there, the chicken-hearted Spanish army refused to sail out to meet them. They were too afraid of eager English attack – foul luck, Phil!

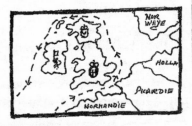

✗ The English sent fire-ships loaded with explosives into the Armada – the Spanish panicked and crashed into each other. They did more damage than the fire-ships! – foul luck, Phil!

✗ The English chased the Spanish clear into the North Sea – that's when God played his ace. Terrific storms ripped the heart out of Phil's fleet – foul luck, Phil!

Reports from Spain say Philip will not be punishing the Armada leaders. The king says the disaster was the will of God. For once he's right! God saved the Queen . . . and now is the time to reward our gallant sailors.

After the Armada

The 'reward' of the English sailors was sickness, poverty or death! As the English admiral, Lord Howard, wrote to the Queen's ministers Walsingham and Burghley . . .

The sailors cry out for money and do not know when they will be paid. They had hoped, after their great service, to receive their pay in full. Finding they have so little makes them very discontent. Sickness and death are beginning to grow amongst us. It is a most pitiful sight to see how the sailors, with no place to go, are dying in the streets. It would grieve any man's heart to see men who have served so bravely die so miserably.

The other effect of the Armada was to make the English more suspicious of the Catholics and especially of the Spaniards.

Philip did not send another Armada against Elizabeth – but the English always feared that he would. That's why spies like Marlowe and Poley worked harder than ever after the Armada to uncover the secrets of the Spanish – especially the ones who still fought in the Netherlands.

Marlowe spent time spying in the Netherlands. Poley was supposed to be there in late June 1593. For some reason he was in Mrs Bull's house in Deptford that week. He was there when Kit Marlowe was stabbed.

The Armada attack came five years before Marlowe's death – but fear of the Catholics, and the need for ruthless spies, was stronger than ever in 1593.

6. THE FAITH FILE

···

Kit Marlowe was about to be charged with 'heresy' — saying that Jesus was not the son of God. His fellow playwright, Thomas Kyd, had already been tortured for having a script that was full of heresies. Was this 'crime' of Kit Marlowe's so serious that someone wanted him dead? Just how seriously did the Tudors take religion?

The cursed queen

In England Elizabeth I's father, Henry VIII, had replaced the 'Catholic' Church with a 'Protestant' Church of England. The difference was that the Church of England banned things they thought were 'magical'. The Protestants didn't believe that a cross, a Bible or a statue of a saint had any powers.

But people were still superstitious.

Queen Elizabeth I fell ill at the end of February 1603. No one is quite sure of her problem because her doctors were not very skilful. Most people believed she was dying from 'a weariness of life'.

There were said to be signs of death all round the dying queen. A phantom which looked exactly like her was seen wandering around the place, even in broad daylight.

This led superstitious people to start rumours of their own. There were two stories about a curse on the queen. One curse was written on a large coin of Welsh gold.

The other curse was said to be a playing card, the queen of hearts. A nail had been pushed through the forehead of the queen's face and pushed to the underside of the chair. This is similar to the witchcraft curse where a wax image of the victim is stuck through with pins – the image gets the nail/pin but the victim suffers the pain.

BUT . . . if it is that easy to kill a victim why were witches caught and executed? Why didn't they simply destroy their accusers with playing cards and curses written on coins?

Aggro at the altar

The Elizabethans feared and hated the devil. On the other hand they were not so respectful of their church either.

In church the Elizabethans sometimes . . .

✝ swore
✝ shouted at the preacher
✝ spat on the floor
✝ drank ale

A country priest once complained:

"The people love a pot of ale better than a pulpit, they love a corn rick better than a church door."

Would such people really have been upset because Kit Marlowe had a copy of a document that said Jesus was not the son of God?

And did you know . . .

✝ that the paper had been copied from a book that had been around for forty years?

✝ that the book had been written by an archbishop called John Assheton?

✝ that the book had never been banned for what it said?

✝ that there was a copy of Assheton's book in the headmaster's library at Marlowe's Canterbury school?

✝ that Thomas Kyd never said Marlowe *wrote* the document – only that it *belonged* to him?

So, Marlowe's religion was enough to get him into trouble with the law. But was it enough for someone to want him dead?

7. TUDOR WOMEN

Tudor girls, like Ellie in the story, did not usually go to school. They were expected to stay at home and learn from their mothers how to be good housewives. If they didn't marry they could still be useful as spinners of wool. Today we still call an unmarried woman a 'spinster'.

Foreign visitors thought English girls and women had a lot of freedom. Here are some facts about Elizabethan women. See if you agree. Would you have liked to have been a woman in those days . . . ?

1. There were one or two boarding schools for girls by the end of the 1500s, but the education there was poor. As one girl said, "All we are ever taught to do is to frisk and dance, to paint our faces or to curl our hair." Some people actually said that to fill a girl's head with Latin and Greek was not necessary, not worth the effort . . . and could damage her brain!

2. Girls would not usually choose their own husbands. A father's job was to choose a good husband for her and see her married between the ages of fourteen and sixteen. In Shakespeare's *Romeo and Juliet*, when the girl tries to choose her own husband, the result is seen as an absolute disaster. The playwright doesn't blame the young couple but the stubborn fathers and the feuding families. Forced marriages were rare – but a girl was expected to fall in love with the man her father chose. If she didn't then she was stuck with him. Divorce was almost unheard of . . . unless you happened to be Henry VIII, of course!

3.   Married life was hard work for a woman. She was expected to manage all the housework – even if she could afford servants to help. And of course she had to make sure the children were brought up properly. Most women had between eight and fifteen children . . . but would probably see many of them die. Henry VIII's first wife, Catherine of Aragon, had nine babies of which only one lived. His third wife, Jane Seymour, gave birth to the son he wanted . . . but died herself shortly after giving birth.

4.   Housework for a married woman would be especially hard because there was no machinery to help. Washing bedclothes, for example, involved scrubbing them with home-made soap in cold water. The weight of the wet sheets would make them a strain to carry. The effort would be exhausting. This is why bed sheets were only washed once every three months. At the end of such a hard day's work the husband would return home and expect to be served his meal while he sat on the best chair at the table – his wife would probably have to make do with a stool. The children often stood to eat their meal!

5. Widows who survived into old age seemed to be the main victims of witch hunts. The Church believed that men or women could be witches. In practice most people accused of witchcraft were women – and most of those were old women. They were 'easy' victims for the town or village bullies. If something went wrong in the district and the devil was suspected then some harmless old woman would be ducked in the river to test her for witchcraft. If she floated then she was a witch and was taken out and hanged; if she sank she was innocent . . . but probably drowned.

So, would you have liked to have been a woman in Elizabethan times?

8. THE CLOTHES FILE

Clothes were important to the Elizabethans. They didn't just keep them warm, they also said a lot about the person wearing the clothes. See how much you know about Elizabethan clothing . . .

True or false

1. A theatre company would give more money for a costume than they would give to a playwright like Marlowe who spent months writing the play. *True/false?*

2. Elizabethan men wore padded jackets to make them look strong and muscular. *True/false?*

3. Queen Elizabeth had seven dresses, crusted with jewels. One for every day of the week. *True/false?*

4. The ruffs that Elizabethans wore around their necks were always white. *True/false?*

5. You could tell if a woman was married by whether or not she wore a hat. *True/false?*

6. University students, like young Kit Marlowe had been, were expected to wear a uniform of a long dark

cloak and hood. *True/false?*

7. People wore the richest clothes they could afford. *True/false?*

8. Some women wore Catherine wheels. *True/false?*

9. Elizabeth I wore woollen stockings. *True/false?*

10. Some women hid their faces behind masks. *True/false?*

Answers

1. **True**. A playwright received a small payment for his play but people came to see action and spectacular sights, not listen to too many words. Audiences loved dazzling costumes and theatre companies paid fortunes to have them made.

2. **True**. The padding also kept them warm in the draughty houses . . . and King James (who followed Elizabeth I) found his padded jacket made a useful dagger-proof body-protector. This stuffing would be horsehair – or even bran horse fodder! – and it weighed up to three kilograms.

3. **False**. She had 2,000 dresses in her wardrobe and most of them were decorated with jewels. She often gave them away when she grew tired of them.

4. **False**. Ruffs were dyed most colours. The most popular for a time was yellow.

5. **True**. A married woman wore a hat (and probably a low-necked dress) when she went out. An unmarried woman went bare-headed (and wore a high-necked dress).

6. **True**. But they didn't always! Many students preferred velvet and silk garments even though it meant a fine. The portrait of Marlowe that hangs in Corpus Christi College at Cambridge shows him wearing brown velvet slashed with pink satin and a fine lace collar. There are gold buttons on his jacket and his hair is far longer than students were allowed. Was Kit Marlowe a rebel?

7.   False. People wore what was most suitable for their job or what they were allowed to wear. There were laws which said only someone of royal blood could wear the colour crimson, the middle classes were allowed to use velvet for their sleeves only and coloured fur could only be worn by the upper classes. A law of 1571 said that everyone over the age of six years had to wear a woollen cap on Sundays and holy days. The wool dealers and clothmakers loved this law – the people who had to wear the hats hated it!

8.   True. A Catherine wheel was worn underneath a skirt. It was a whale-bone hoop that made the skirt stand out from the hips.

9.   False. Elizabeth was said to be the first woman in England to wear silk stockings. Once she'd tried them on she swore she would never wear any other type. Of course they then became the most fashionable stockings for the rich Elizabethans. The poor stuck to woollen ones.

10. True. This prevented their faces from becoming suntanned – for a dark skin was unfashionable. There was no elastic to fasten a mask around the head, so a button would be sewn on to the inside of the mask. This button would be held between the teeth so the hands were left free. It must have made talking difficult!

How does knowledge about Elizabethan clothes help us investigate the death of Kit Marlowe? Look at this fact about the men's fashion of wearing daggers and see . . .

The deadly dagger

An Elizabethan man would wear
a dagger in a sheath attached
to his belt.

The dagger was worn on the
right and slightly to the back.

The tip of the dagger was
held up by a chain so the dagger
was horizontal and it could be
drawn quickly.

The Marlowe murder

Frizer said that Kit Marlowe came
up behind him and took his (Frizer's)
dagger from his belt. This would
not be easy to do from behind, as
you can see.

Marlowe used the handle of the
dagger to beat Frizer on the head so the
point would be turned towards Marlowe's own face. That
was how Marlowe was stabbed in the eye. But Marlowe
would have had to turn the dagger round to do this – a slow
and clumsy movement. What did Frizer do to stop him?

If Marlowe *had* intended to kill Frizer he'd have used the
point, not the handle . . . so Frizer went a bit far in killing
Marlowe in 'self defence'.

Frizer, Skeres and Poley came up with this 'self-defence'
story at the inquest into Marlowe's death. The coroner
believed it happened that way. Do you?

Part Three
The truth about
Kit Marlowe

"Kit Marlowe was a spy for the queen ever since he was a student at Cambridge," Ellie explained patiently the next morning. My joints still ached but there was nothing broken. Ellie explained how she had asked everyone she knew where I'd been taken. By chance one of the jailers was drinking in the Swan and mentioned seeing a boy lying on the rack in Poley's torture room.

"So Kit Marlowe did go to Rheims Catholic College?" I asked.

"He did. But he went as a spy for the queen's secret service."

"That's how he came to have such powerful friends," I said.

"And powerful friends make for powerful enemies. In the end they made a plot to get rid of Marlowe. First they posted that poem on the wall of the Dutch church," Ellie said.

"They left clues that it was by Marlowe and hoped he'd be arrested."

"That's right," she agreed. "His powerful friends kept him out of prison yet again. Remember the law had tried to lock him away for helping to murder young Bradley in the street fight – then they'd tried to arrest him for forgery. Each time he got away with it. Now the Dutch church poem failed to get Marlowe locked away."

"So they used Marlowe's blasphemy notes in Kyd's room?" I said.

Ellie shook her head. "There was no blasphemy note in Kyd's room. First they arrested Kyd . . . then they said they'd found those notes in his papers. They probably planted them there. They weren't in Marlowe's handwriting. No one said they belonged to Marlowe."

"Except Kyd," I argued.

"Except Kyd," she agreed. "But he was being tortured. After a couple of days on the rack he'd say anything they wanted him to say."

I remembered the rack and shuddered. Of course she was right. "It would be Kyd's word against Marlowe's. That plot against him wouldn't work. He'd get away again."

"So they had to murder him in the end," I said.

"That's right," Ellie sighed.

"Who was Poley's master? Who was the real killer? Who gave the orders?" I asked.

The girl shrugged. "I don't suppose we'll ever know. All we know is that Marlowe was a friend of the great Walter Raleigh – and Raleigh's enemy is the Duke of Essex. It could have been him, but of course Poley will never admit that."

I began to tremble again at the thought of Poley and his cold-fire irons in the basket. They'd killed the queen's spy Marlowe without a second thought. They'd kill a boy actor like . . . like a fly, as Mr Shakespeare said.

Ellie seemed to read my thoughts. "Mr Shakespeare says that if we change your name and your appearance you can stay with the company. Play men's parts in future. You should be safe. You'll just have to act as if you are someone else – you should manage it since you're an actor."

"But not a very good one," I sniffed. "According to you."

"Well," she said coyly. "Not as good as me."

"You?"

She gave a wicked grin. "Who do you think played the part of Juliet while you were on Poley's little rack?"

"You? You can't! Women can't . . ."

"No, John. Women can. Women can do anything if you men will only let us."

She turned and walked out of the door with the sort of proud walk a boy actor can never copy . . . even a good boy actor.

EPILOGUE

Ellie and John are fictional characters and it's unlikely that William Shakespeare ever investigated the death of Christopher Marlowe in this way.

But the facts behind the stabbing are true. It is the way that people have looked at those facts that has changed over the centuries. These are a few of the interpretations:

Marlowe died because he was a vicious troublemaker. He attacked Frizer but died when Frizer defended himself. Frizer, Poley and Skeres were innocent of any crime. This is the story told at the time and repeated in most books about Marlowe.

Marlowe died because he knew too much. He was guilty of the blasphemy charge and was about to be tortured for it. Under torture he might have revealed lots of dangerous information about his friends – friends like Walter Raleigh. So Marlowe was killed on the orders of his *friends*.

Marlowe wasn't killed at all:

- The spelling of Marlowe's name varied in his lifetime – Marlin, Marly, Marley and Morley were common spellings. There was a second 'Christopher Morley' at Cambridge at the same time as the playwright we know as Marlowe. It was this *other* Christopher Morley who died at Mrs Bull's house.

- He faced torture for the blasphemy charge. His friends faked his death and he retired to lead a quiet life in the countryside. He died a year later and was buried in an unmarked grave.

- He faced torture for the blasphemy charge. His friends faked his death and he left the country. There he kept on writing plays. He sent the plays across to England where a friend produced them under a false name. What name? William Shakespeare. Many people believe that Marlowe lived and wrote Shakespeare's plays.

Marlowe died because he was tangled in the world of spying. He had some deadly enemies who failed to get him arrested so ended up killing him. (This is the idea put forward in this story.)

We'll never be able to prove any of these ideas. You just have to look at the evidence and decide which is the most likely? Which do you think?

It's a true mystery of history.